To my father, Michael la Forest Wyatt, who taught me about unconditional love for all animals and to my son, J. Michael Hutchinson, who brought the real Abby home.   WW

To my friend, Carol, whose heart and soul, as well as her photographs, are in this book. We miss you.   GB

To Arthur, Gen, Whitney, and of course, Savannah.   CM

Acknowledgements

My deepest appreciation to the enthusiastic children who appear in this book: A.J. Muti, Morgan McCormack, Michael Falduto, Daneisha Whitson, Baron Beston, Jason Leeds, Alyson Moy, and Annie Pedersen. Also, to the accommodating adults: Art Muti, Joseph Mola, Kathy Pedersen, and Adrian "Duke" Smith.

It is with gratitude I wish to thank all those whose quotes, eloquently and with sincerity endorse the message in this book.

To Cassie and Carl Segal — Your generosity will touch the lives of many animals. I am blessed by your presence in my life.

To Mary and Michael Weist, breeders of the world-renowned Beechcroft Labrador retrievers and the real Abby the Labby. You and the pups were there when we needed you.

Many thanks to The Seeing Eye® for approval of the manuscript and photo set-up; to St. Hubert's Animal Welfare Center for training Abby to be a dog worthy of inspiration; to Marnie Vyff of AltaGraphics for her superior art talent and undying patience, and to HP and Co. and AFS for the guiding hand.

I am grateful for the editorial assistance and enthusiastic support from the following people: Dorothy Ryan, Carolyn Yoder, Sharon Cerchiaro, Charlotte Longo, my SCBWI writer's groups, Barbara Winson, Nancy Hassanein, Joan White, Maria Mensinger, Jessica Loos, Rebecca Santana, Eileen Hutchinson, Loren Spiotta-DiMare, Karen E. Quinones Miller, Barbara Bertschy, Monica Butler, Marty Friedman, and Vivien Bliss Wyatt.

For their love, understanding, and assistance throughout this project, I thank my good friend, Deborah Martin, and my husband, Peter Loos.

And, thank you to all the others along the way; you know who you are.

ISBN 0-9764773-0-0
LCCN 2005901099

Copyright © 2005 by Wendy Wyatt

Published by
AbbyLab Press, LLC
10 Center Drive
Mountain Lakes, NJ 07046
Telephone/Fax 973-316-6843
www.abbylabpress.com

10 9 8 7 6 5 4 3 2 1
First Edition

Printed by Seaber Turner Associates Book Manufacturing - Blandon, PA

Book Design and Photographic Coloration
Marnie K. Vyff of AltaGraphics, LLC

Please Don't Hurt Abby the Labby!

To Maggie —
(Remember Abby!
Wendy Wyatt

by
Wendy Wyatt

Photographs
Carol Max and Gayle Burns

Photographic Coloration
Marnie K. Vyff

Sam loves the Labrador retriever puppy his family gave him for his birthday. He names her Abby the Labby and puts a red collar around her neck. It looks and fits just right.

Sam's baby sister, Sara, loves Abby, too. But when the puppy sniffs her sticky fingers, Sara pulls Abby's ears.

Startled, Abby yelps!

"Let go, Sara!" Sam calls out as he moves her hands away from Abby. "Mom, Dad, help! Come quick!"

"Sara, please don't hurt Abby," Mom says firmly.

"Your sister is still a baby, Sam. She thinks Abby's just another toy. Why don't you teach her how to pet the puppy?"

"Look," Sam shows Sara, "see how Abby likes it when you're gentle with her?"

Sara laughs as Abby licks her cheek.

"You see," says Dad smiling, "the kinder we are to her, the more she'll love us. Abby can't tell us in words when she's unhappy or if she's hurt. She trusts that we'll protect her from harm — just like you protected her, Sam."

"I want Abby to grow up to be the best dog ever, but taking good care of a puppy is hard work. Isn't it, Dad?"

"It sure is, Sam. We need to . . .

feed Abby just as we feed you,

bathe her just as we bathe you,

play with Abby just as we play with you and . . .

most of all, we need to hug Abby the
Labby just as we hug you."

Later that day, Dad says, "Let's go and meet some special dogs who were raised as puppies with the same good care we're giving Abby."

"Why are they so special?" asks Sam.

"Because these dogs grew into loving and loyal pets," replies Dad.

"They also help people in important ways," explains Mom. "It's called service work."

On the way, they see how Sunny, an official Seeing Eye guide dog, serves as a pair of eyes for Mrs. Max.

Sunny helps Mrs. Max, who is blind, to walk safely through stores, along crowded sidewalks, and across busy streets. It is important not to pet Sunny when she is wearing her harness because that means she is working.

When they visit a home for senior citizens, Sam watches how Sparky, a therapy dog, shares his love with people who want a friend. Sparky likes to snuggle on Mr. Martin's lap, and Mr. Martin always has a few dog biscuits for Sparky in his pocket.

On the way home, they meet Rocky, a police dog, who is Officer Gallo's canine partner. Rocky not only protects Officer Gallo but also uses his nose for search and rescue missions. With extra training, Rocky could even detect the scent of dangerous substances or help track down criminals.

"Dogs like these are more than friends," says Dad.

Mom agrees. "People depend on them everyday to make their lives better."

The next afternoon, Sam sees his friends at the park. He proudly shows them his new puppy.

They are so excited that they push to grab and hold her. Some in the group are too rough, and their voices are too loud.

Frightened, Abby whimpers.

Sam quickly picks her up and cries out, "Please don't hurt Abby the Labby!"

Sam gently pets Abby. "It's okay," he whispers to her. "They didn't mean to scare you."

"Abby has feelings just like we do," Sam explains to his friends. "She can't talk in words when she's sad or hurt. So, we have to watch out for her and keep her safe."

Sam tells them about the special dogs he saw on his walk the day before. "If we want Abby to grow up to be friendly and loving just like those dogs we have to be kind to her as a puppy."

"I'm sorry if I hurt her," apologizes his friend Matt. "Can I pet Abby again? I'll be gentle."

"Me, too!" begs Olivia.

"And me!" adds Alex.

"Hey, Sam, we'll look out for Abby, too," promises Matt. "If we ever see anybody being mean to her, we will all shout . . .

'Please don't hurt Abby the Labby!'"